INSTRUCTOR'S MANUAL TO ACCOMPANY

BASIC MATHEMATICAL CONCEPTS

F. Lynwood Wren
Professor of Mathematics
San Fernando Valley State College

McGraw-Hill Book Company
New York / St. Louis / San Francisco
Toronto / London / Sydney

Instructor's Manual to accompany Basic Mathematical Concepts

Copyright © 1965 by McGraw-Hill, Inc. All Rights Reserved.
Printed in the United States of America. The contents, or parts
thereof, may be reproduced for use with BASIC MATHEMATICAL
CONCEPTS, by F. Lynwood Wren, provided such reproductions
bear copyright notice, but may not be reproduced in any form for
any other purpose without permission of the publishers.

71906

1234567890WH7210698765

INTRODUCTION

This book has been written for the primary purpose of helping those individuals, who have a limited mathematical background, acquire some understanding of the language and structure of elementary mathematics. The first six chapters are devoted to a study of the structure of the number systems which enable us to deal effectively with the quantitative situations we experience from day to day. A theme running through these chapters is the tremendous significance of place value in our decimal system of numerals.

An effort is made to make it clear that the number systems we use have significant logical structure. There are sets of undefined elements with well-defined operations. The use of these operations is controlled by certain postulated properties and derived theorems. It is made very clear that the postulates are no more than basic assumptions that shape the behavior of the elements under the operations defined for their use. However, effort also is made to make it just as clear that these assumptions are not "plucked out of thin air," as it were, but that they have a firm rooting in the fertile soil of intuitive acceptability.

After the first chapter builds a necessary vocabulary for the language we wish to use, the second chapter presents some of the more important of the historically significant numeration systems. This is done to provide a background against which one can acquire a richer understanding of the structure of our decimal system of numeration.

Chapter 3 then undertakes a study of the simplest of the number systems we use, namely, the natural number system. Many of its properties are developed before pointing out its inadequacies which confront us with a need for extending to other number systems. These necessary extensions are then pursued through Chapters 4, 5, and 6. Finally, in Chapter 6 we are able to present in proper perspective the impressive diagram of the number systems of elementary mathematics.

Chapter 7 presents a new form of arithmetic, known as calendar arithmetic or, more mathematically, as modular arithmetic. This short interlude is introduced for three purposes: (1) to present a new and interesting type of arithmetic which has great potential for motivation at lower levels of instruction; (2) to present one of the simplest of all mathematical systems, a group; and (3) to present a very simple technique for devising tests for divisibility.

Chapter 8 directs the attention of the reader to a study of many of the elementary but very fundamental concepts of geometry. These are organized and presented under the major heads of position, shape, and size. This development is purely intuitive. The objective is to give the reader an informed orientation in the contemporary structure of these concepts that will provide for him a better understanding of his quantitative environment.

Chapter 9 then looks at the problems and techniques of measurement. Emphasis is given to the approximate nature of measurement and the need for learning how to make appropriate measurements, compute with approximate numbers, and interpret the results obtained from such computation. Attention is paid to both direct and indirect forms of measurement, also to both the English and metric systems of weights and measures.

Finally, there are no more important concepts in all of mathematics than those of relation and function. Chapter 10 directs attention to a study of these two fundamental concepts within the limitations of the linear function, the linear equation, and linear inequalities. An important final section of this chapter deals with the fundamental problem of building an efficient pattern of attack on the verbal problem.

Two distinct features of the book are to be found in the Guidelines for Careful Study, which introduce each chapter, and the Invitations to Extended Study, which close each chapter. The intent of the guidelines is to provide questions that direct pertinent review of previous chapters and outline the more significant content of the forthcoming chapter. They attempt to motivate intelligent study by providing continuity and arousing curiosity. Furthermore, they provide a checklist on retention of information, which can be used as an effective learning device. The teacher should make every effort to help the student learn how to use these lists of questions to best advantage.

The Invitations to Extended Study are designed to encourage interested individuals to pursue lines of thought beyond the confines of the text. They are at the end of each chapter, and consist of selected exercises that are a bit more difficult than those of the text, suggested projects related to the chapter, and additional reading related to but beyond the limitations of the chapter. The bibliography, at the end of the book, is a rich storehouse of related works from which significant help can be obtained. Interested individuals should be encouraged to pursue their study along such avenues of learning or others these may suggest.

The book is designed to provide material for two three-unit semester courses of 45 class periods each. The outline presented in the subsequent pages of this manual suggests an eight-lesson pattern for the book. This will allow a flexibility of ten class periods, five per semester, to provide for tests. The first five chapters provide the program for the first semester and the last five chapters for the second semester.

CHAPTER OUTLINES AND SCHEDULES

CHAPTER 1.   THE NATURE OF NUMBER
(4 lessons)

The two underlying purposes of this chapter are (1) to build a fundamental vocabulary for use in the study of the entire book, and (2) to build an awareness of the need for and the basic significance of number names and number symbols.

Lesson 1. (Sec. 1-1 to the middle of page 6)
Before entering into a discussion of the text material the teacher should call the students' attention to the guidelines. These can be used as preview of the chapter. Each student should be encouraged to use them not only as a guide, indicating what to seek out for careful study, but also as a checklist to be used after completion of the chapter to check on retention of information.

Pay careful attention to each word in the vocabulary of sets. Use several different illustrations, both teacher-made and student-made, of each concept.

Lesson 2. (Completion of Sec. 1-1)
Here attention is paid to union, intersection, and complementation in the use of sets. The concepts of the empty set and of disjoint sets need particular attention. The use of Venn diagrams should be encouraged as an aid to the understanding of the operation on sets.

It is suggested that time be taken for working all exercises at the end of this section. Most of this can be oral. If desirable, some exercises can be used for written homework.

Lesson 3. (Secs. 1-2 and 1-3)
These two sections develop the concepts of cardinal number and ordinal number. Give very careful emphasis to the fundamental concept of one-to-one correspondence. Also emphasize the fact that zero (0) is used as a number as well as a placeholder. There can very well be some students for whom this is an entirely new idea.

Lesson 4. (Sec. 1-4)
One of the difficult lessons for the student to learn thoroughly is that our numerals are symbols representing numbers and not the numbers themselves. This section, by using unfamiliar symbols and an unfamiliar base for grouping, concentrates on this problem. A good teaching technique is to have the class assume that they belong to a race of people with no number names or number symbolism and then ask someone to start to count off to determine an answer to the question, "How many people are in

1

this class?" In order to provide a significant foundation for later work it is well to postulate for the students the principle of place value and the additive principle so fundamental in the structure of our numerals. If this technique is used, do not allow the use of the familiar number names "one," "two," etc., nor of the familiar numerals of our numeration system. Instead, guide the students into the use of the names and symbols of the verto system of this section.

Before leaving the chapter, encourage the use of the listed suggestions for further study. Some are sufficiently simple to be assigned to some of the students. Exercises 4 and 5 are designed to extend reading by the better students beyond the text.

Chapter 2. SYSTEMS OF NUMERATION
(5 lessons)

There was a fourfold purpose in the writing of this chapter: (1) to present certain historically significant primitive systems of numeration that they might be contrasted with our system; (2) to underscore the importance of place value in the structure of our numerals; (3) to analyze the basic structure of the decimal system of numeration; and (4) to use bases other than ten to build a system of numerals for the purpose of under scoring the significance of the concept of the use of a base for grouping purposes.

Lesson 1. (Secs. 2-1 and 2-2)
Again emphasis should be given first to the use of the guidelines as an outlined preview of the chapter and as a checklist to measure retention of learning.

The four primitive numeration systems are cited as illustrations of the tremendous handicap inherent in a numeration system that does not use the principle of place value in the formation of numerals.

Lesson 2. (Sec. 2-3)
The Mayan system is presented as the earliest known system to have a zero symbol and to use the principles of place value and addition in the building of numerals. This is a good place to begin the study of equivalent numerals.

Lesson 3. (Secs. 2-4, 2-5, and 2-6)
In these sections the basic structure of the decimal system of numeration is analyzed. Careful attention should be paid to the illustration used to point out the distinction between and importance of digit value and place value for digit symbols in the shaping of numerals for use in dealing with large numbers. Facility in the use of exponents as an aid in giving expression to the place value of each different position in a numeral needs to be developed.

Lesson 4. (Secs. 2-7, 2-8, and 2-9)
A very important aid to fuller understanding of the significance of

a base in numeration and of our use of ten as a base can be found in the
use of bases other than ten to build numerals. These sections introduce
this concept. A clear understanding of the import of these three sections
is basic to a great deal of the development of the next four chapters.

Lesson 5. (Sec. 2-10)

The concept of equivalent numerals in different bases is fundamental in the building of a clear understanding of the fact that numerals
are merely symbols for numbers—and not numbers. This is an important
section as it is basic to much of the work of subsequent chapters.

The Invitations to Extended Study offer suggestions for further efforts
either in the study of other important contemporary numeration systems
or in a search into the historical background of our decimal system.

CHAPTER 3. THE NATURAL NUMBER SYSTEM
(8 lessons)

In this chapter, for the first time, the guidelines serve for a review as well as for a preview and a checklist. Also it is with this chapter
that the serious study of number systems begins. Both historically and
realistically the natural number system is the number system of first experience. Its basic postulates are well oriented in intuitive acceptance.
They should be so presented and developed. Only after this has been accomplished and a clear comprehension of the nature of implication and
proof has been developed should the task of logical derivation of other
properties be undertaken.

Lesson 1. (Secs. 3-1, 3-2, 3-3, and 3-4)

These four sections are designed to clarify what is meant by the
phrase "natural number," develop the concept of the structure of a number system, and define what the operation of addition is as applied to
natural numbers.

Lesson 2. (Secs. 3-5 and 3-6)

The first of these two sections presents a bit of the historical background out of which our modern addition algorithm has evolved. The
student should be guided to a realization of the simplicity and efficiency
that place value brings to the algorithm.

The second section undertakes to build an intuitive orientation of
the basic properties of natural numbers under addition. This study should
be pursued with care. The use of different bases can be very helpful. The
characteristic properties of the relation of equality are presented. Care
should be taken to see that they are understood and that their significance
is appreciated.

Lesson 3. (Secs. 3-6 and 3-7)

Section 3-6 will demand additional attention before going on to study
the techniques of checking addition. The principal instructional medium to
be used in this lesson is the full use of the exercises at the end of Section

3-7. Much of this should be oral for review and checkup purposes. This should be accompanied by a good thorough written assignment.

Lesson 4. (Secs. 3-8 and 3-9)

The two well-defined operations of the natural number system are addition and multiplication. These two sections proceed with the definition of multiplication. The most elementary approach is to relate multiplication to addition, just as addition was related to the more fundamental operation of counting. This should be carefully developed before passing on to the more general definition based on the concept of the cartesian product of two sets.

Lesson 5. (Secs. 3-10, 3-11, and 3-12)

After the definition of multiplication in the preceding section, these sections proceed to develop the process as a well-defined operation controlled by certain intuitively acceptable properties and with well-established checks.

Lesson 6. (Sec. 3-13)

Here proficiency in the operations of addition and multiplication is one of the objectives. This is not accomplished through refresher practice in the context of familiar base-ten numerals, but in the more challenging and constructive context of computing equivalent numerals in different bases.

Lesson 7. (Secs. 3-14 and 3-15)

Here for the first time the full set of postulates of the natural number system is presented. These postulates should be studied analytically and critically to make sure that there is complete understanding of what they are and how they are to be used. This should be accomplished before proceeding to a discussion of the nature of proof. In this context only the basic nature of implication is discussed.

This is a very critical lesson and should be developed with great care and caution.

Lesson 8. (Sec. 3-16)

In this section four of the basic theorems of the natural number system are proved. A few others are stated as exercises. No attempt whatsoever is made to be exhaustive in this development. Rather the idea is to be illustrative and to give the student some experience in the exercise of deductive techniques. This lesson will present distinct difficulties which must be dealt with carefully. In fact, they cannot be overcome within the limitations of one lesson. They must be pursued continually.

Among the invitations which close the chapter there are listed still other theorems, some of which are sufficiently advanced to call upon the principle of finite induction. The techniques of deduction also are pursued further.

CHAPTER 4. THE DOMAIN OF INTEGERS
(8 lessons)

Subtraction, the operation which is inversely related to addition, very naturally enters the discussions with natural numbers. The fact that closure under this operation is no longer a characteristic of the system leads to the necessity for extending the set of numbers to the set of all integers. This in turn calls for a "re-tooling" of the definitions of addition and multiplication to retain all previously acquired properties while gaining more liberal uses and interpretations.

The review aspect of the guidelines attains its full stature with this chapter. The first five questions are of great importance in the preparation for intelligent study of the content of Chapter 4. This should be made quite clear to the student.

Lesson 1. (Secs. 4-1, 4-2, and 4-3 only through the definition of "additive inverse")

In these sections we meet the first extension of the number system. Subtraction is introduced, and should be developed carefully in its relation to addition. Zero as the additive identity and the concept of additive inverse are two new concepts introduced. They must be presented very carefully and in full detail.

Lessons 2-4. (Sec. 4-3)

This section is the key to this entire chapter. The concepts of additive inverse, positive and negative integers, and zero as an integer must be developed in very deliberate detail. The proof of each theorem presented is of great importance.

Lesson 5. (Secs. 4-4 and 4-5)

In Theorem 4-7 the full significance of subtraction as the inverse operation to addition is developed. This is important and should be studied carefully. Opportunity for analysis of the different forms of the subtraction algorithm is provided.

Lessons 6-8. (Sec. 4-6)

The postulates of the domain of integers should be studied in contrast with those of the natural number system. The similarities and differences should be examined carefully and understood thoroughly.

Each theorem should be analyzed and, in particular, those on inequalities.

The concepts of prime and composite numbers, factorization and the greatest common factor, and even and odd numbers are essential to full understanding and use of integers.

Along with additional theorems about integers, the Invitations to Extended Study call attention to perfect numbers and amicable numbers, concepts that are of historical significance.

CHAPTER 5. THE FIELD OF RATIONAL NUMBERS
(15 lessons)

The concepts of division, quotient, and multiplicative inverse lead to the necessity for a second extension of our number system to incorporate rational numbers. The accompanying modification of the definitions of addition and multiplication gives a more general interpretation of these operations. There must be continual emphasis on the fact that in such extensions of definition neither operation loses any of its characteristics acquired in the study of integers or natural numbers. With the new set of postulates, from one point of view, our number system has now reached full growth in that the rational numbers with addition and multiplication constitute a number field. This is one of the most important concepts in mathematics.

Again the first five guideline questions constitute a pertinent review in preparation for the study of this chapter.

Lessons 1-3. (Sec. 5-1)

This is the key section to this entire chapter. The concept of rational number is defined along with the operations on rational numbers. Each definition, postulate, and theorem should be analyzed in full detail. It is suggested that all of the exercises at the end of this section be worked. Give particular attention to the discussion of the fact that division by zero is undefined.

Lesson 4. (Secs. 5-2 and 5-3)

The nature and language of division are presented first, and then the division algorithm. This algorithm is important as a basic concept, and facility in its use is essential for the study of Sec. 5-4 and all of Chapter 7. Abundant practice in its use should be required of all students.

Lesson 5. (Sec. 5-4)

The Euclidean algorithm is an important technique for use in problems of factorization.

Lesson 6. (Sec. 5-5)

Conversion by division of numerals in a given base to equivalent numerals in other bases offers great opportunities for developing significant appreciation and understanding of place value. The content of this section should be developed with this in mind.

Lesson 7. (Sec. 5-6)

As mentioned previously, the concept of a number field is one of the most important concepts in all of mathematics. The rational numbers offer the first opportunity for full development of the concept. The definitions and postulates of this section must be studied with great care.

Lesson 8. (Secs. 5-7, 5-8, and 5-9)

Before entering into a discussion of the use of rational numbers as fractions, it would be well to review in some detail the basic definition of a rational number and the definitions of the operations with rational numbers.

Lesson 9. (Secs. 5-10 and 5-11)

A review of the field properties and order relations as applied to rational numbers would be in place here before undertaking the study of the use of fractions in computation and as symbols for ratios. A discussion of proportion should be developed along with the concept of ratio.

Lesson 10. (Secs. 5-12 and 5-13)
Emphasize the fact that the set of all decimal fractions is a proper subset of all fractions. Any principles developed for fractions in general also apply to decimal fractions. Place value offers the simplified notation for decimal fractions, and computation with decimal fractions is much simpler than with common fractions. The exponential equivalents for the place values of relative positions in a decimal fraction needs full attention. The concepts of finite and infinite decimals are important for later use.

Lesson 11. (Sec. 5-14)
Since computing with decimals is essentially the same as computing with integers, the major problem of this section is the building of techniques to protect against the improper placement and use of the decimal point. It should be remembered that its function in a numeral is simply to single out and locate ones position.

Lesson 12. (Sec. 5-15)
The techniques for predicting the type of decimal into which a given common fraction will convert can be made interesting, challenging, and beneficial. It has a great deal of significance as preliminary ground work for Chapter 6.

Lesson 13. (Sec. 5-16)
The inverse process of converting finite and infinite repeating decimals into rational numbers (the quotients of two integers) is also a significant technique. The order of development in this section is essential for simplicity of treatment.
The full significance of Sections 5-15 and 5-16 is summarized in the statement of Postulate 5-5. Do not overlook the last paragraph of this section and its restatement as Exercise 8 in the final set of exercises. The full significance of this exercise will become very evident in Chapter 6.

Lesson 14. (Secs. 5-17, 5-18, and 5-19)
Percentage is but a special topic of decimal fractions. Per cents are but two-place decimals and, consequently, they are merely fractions whose denominators are 100. No new techniques need to be developed. There is only the problem of keeping aware of the fact that any percentage problem is related to some number, called the base. This can modify the entire texture of any percentage problem.
The percentage formula is of all importance. It simply states that in any percentage problem there are only three numbers involved. One of these numbers, the percentage, is the product of two others, the rate and the base. If the product is unknown, then the process to be used is multiplication; otherwise, the process is division.

Lesson 15. (Semester Review)
This last lesson of the semester should be reserved for a concentrated oral review of the semester's work. This will thus cover the first

five chapters of the book. It is quite possible that one might wish to enter Chapter 6 for a brief study of real numbers before closing out the semester.

CHAPTER 6. THE NUMBER FIELD OF ELEMENTARY MATHEMATICS
(5 lessons)

This chapter can be used to serve a dual purpose: as the final summarizing chapter for the first-semester program and as the introductory chapter laying the foundation for the second-semester program. A brief sketching of the necessity for further extensions of the number system to include irrational and complex numbers will offer the opportunity to use the diagram of the number systems of elementary mathematics as an effective aid in the review of the work of the first semester. A detailed and careful study of this chapter is essential to the thorough understanding of the second half of the book.

Lesson 1. (Secs. 6-1 and 6-2)
The introductory discussion of the inversely related operations of raising to powers and extraction of roots is essential to the development of this chapter. Take particular precautions that the implications of exponents and root symbols are clearly understood.

Section 6-1 makes use of the pattern of indirect proof to exhibit the existence of irrational numbers as certain types of numbers which are not rational. Both aspects of the theorem are of sufficient importance to demand careful and deliberate development of the proof.

Postulate 6-1 of Section 6-2 should be tied in with Postulate 5-5 of Section 5-16 to draw the contrast between the decimal representation of rational and irrational numbers. This is important as preparation for Sections 6-3 and 6-4.

Lesson 2. (Sec. 6-3)
The absence of closure for irrational numbers under the field operation, Postulates 6-2 and 6-2', and the real number line are all very important concepts to be developed in this lesson. Pay careful attention to the discussion of order on the number line presented in the last paragraph of this section.

Lesson 3. (Sec. 6-4)
Review the field postulates and establish the fact that the set of all real numbers with addition and multiplication constitute a field. Also note the properties of positive real numbers. The concepts of absolute value and interval are of significance not only to the development of this chapter, but also to the development of later chapters. It is essential that they be understood.

Lesson 4. (Sec. 6-5)
Although this is a short section, it requires full detail of development. For some the concept of complex number will be new, and for many

it will require thorough review. Pursue a detailed analysis of the field properties. Difficulty with the multiplicative inverse and the process of division can be anticipated.

Lesson 5. (Sec. 6-6)

This section should be used for pointed review in the context of the diagram of the number systems of elementary mathematics. The development of the text has been to build from the natural numbers up to the complex numbers. It is desirable here to build the diagram by starting with the complex numbers and indicate how restrictions lead through the chain of proper subsets to natural numbers.

There are several interesting and valuable suggestions for additional study in the Invitations to Extended Study. In particular these exercises can be used to give greater significance to the concepts of irrational number and complex number.

CHAPTER 7. MODULAR ARITHMETIC
(3 lessons)

As indicated earlier the three purposes of this short chapter are (1) to give a brief introduction to a novel, and yet very significant form of arithmetic; (2) to present the important concept of a group; and (3) to develop some very practical tests for divisibility.

Lesson 1. (Sec. 7-1)

Analyze very carefully the definition of a group and show how it differs from a field. It is important here to point out that although the same set of elements might constitute an abelian group under addition and also under multiplication, it still might not constitute a field due to absence of the distributive property.

Lesson 2. (Secs. 7-2 and 7-3)

Section 7-2 develops the basic ideas of modular arithmetic under the familiar cloak of using a calendar. The more general concept is reserved for Section 7-3. Definitions 7-3 and 7-4 are basic. Students should build several computational tables under different moduli as part of their responsibility in the study of these two sections.

Lesson 3. (Sec. 7-4)

Here the techniques of modular arithmetic are put to good use in developing effective divisibility tests. Students should be encouraged to check divisibility by other numbers not discussed here.

Modular arithmetic in bases other than ten and proofs of a few significant theorems from group theory are challenging suggestions to be found in the extended study section.

CHAPTER 8. THE CONCEPTS OF POSITION, SHAPE, AND SIZE
(10 lessons)

This chapter introduces a break in the narrative of number which

has characterized the previous seven chapters. It is desirable to take a
look at some of the basic concepts of Euclidean geometry before we seek
to use number as a means for quantifying geometric configurations. While
this treatment is primarily intuitive in nature, attention is paid to the
basic postulates, and some of the simpler theorems are proved. A very
important section of the chapter is devoted to Euclidean constructions,
namely those possible using only straightedge and compass.

Lesson 1. (Secs. 8-1 and 8-2)
    The concepts of point and line are fundamental to an understanding
of the entire chapter. No effort is made to define "point," and "line" is
described merely as a set of points. Since lines, planes, and space are defined as sets of points, it becomes all-important that the vocabulary of
sets be revitalized for ready use. Throughout this lesson and many of the
remaining lessons there occur definitions and postulates that are fundamental to the sequence of development. No one of them should be treated
lightly. Also it is important to note the notation used. This is carefully
developed in the context of accepted modern practice.

Lesson 2. (Sec. 8-3)
    This lesson lays the foundation for thinking in a space of three
dimensions. The concepts of half plane, skew lines, parallel lines and
planes, intersecting lines and planes, and convex set are fundamental to
the chapter.

Lesson 3. (Sec. 8-4)
    The language and symbolism necessary to talk about and work with
angles is developed in this section. Also, the use of positive numbers as
angle measures is discussed. Note the definition of angle and of its measure. Treat the plane and space concepts with equal importance. The several definitions, postulates, and theorems demand careful study to produce
understanding and facility in use. The concept of congruent angles as
angles that have the same measure is introduced.

Lesson 4. (Sec. 8-5 and 8-6)
    The cartesian frame of reference and its use as an aid in the study
of position in the plane and in space is of importance not only here but
also for Chapter 10. Give detailed attention to its fundamentals as presented in Section 8-5 before passing to the adaptation to the earth's surface
in Section 8-6. The careful study of time zones can be made very interesting and beneficial.

Lesson 5. (Sec. 8-7)
    In this section the basic plane and solid figures are defined and dis-
cussed. The classification of triangles and of quadrilaterals should be
studied very carefully. The concept of simple closed curves is also very
fundamental.

Lesson 6. (Sec. 8-8)
    The relation of similarity is one of the most important of all rela-
tions between geometric configurations. The two examples establish

principles for dealing with similarity between triangles. This same technique can be adapted to other similar polygons.

Lesson 7. (Secs. 8-9 and 8-10)

Number again is introduced, this time as a measure of size. The concept of congruent geometric figures as figures that are the same in shape and size is of great importance and demands careful development. Note the three postulates for congruence of triangles.

Although not a great deal is said about symmetry here, it is an important concept when we are dealing with geometric configurations. The more basic criteria are presented in this brief discussion.

Lesson 8-9. (Sec. 8-11)

In this section the fundamental constructions with straightedge and compass are presented. They are called Euclidean constructions because of the fact that three of the fundamental postulates of Euclidean geometry provide for the use of the straightedge (or unmarked ruler) and the compass. These postulates are: (1) A straight line may be drawn from any point to any point. (2) A finite straight line may be produced continuously in a straight line. (3) A circle may be described with any center and distance. (See Section 8-12.)

Postulates 8-15 and 8-16 should be analyzed very carefully before entering into the study of any of the basic constructions. Each construction should be studied in careful detail. Additional constructions are provided in the exercises. All constructions should be proved, and their limitations should be discussed.

Lesson 10. (Sec. 8-12)

This section presents a very brief discussion of the basic postulational differences between Euclidean and non-Euclidean geometries. Also a brief reference is made to the Klein pattern of classifying geometries on the basis of invariants under a group of transformations. In the modern emphasis on mathematical structure, such concepts are of fundamental importance.

Additional theorems and constructions as well as additional analytic properties offer variety of direction to extended study opportunities for this chapter.

CHAPTER 9. THE CONCEPT OF MEASUREMENT
(11 lessons)

After a few spotted definitions and uses of particular measures in Chapter 8, this chapter undertakes a careful study of the entire concept of measurement. The first six questions of the guidelines recall from previous chapters bits of information pertinent to the study of Chapter 9. No new numbers are necessary for the problems of measurement, but there is need for a careful study of the use and interpretation of numbers as they are used to indicate the approximations arising from measurement. Some of these problems can become troublesome if not approached with precaution.

Lesson 1. (Secs. 9-1 and 9-2)
These two sections concentrate on the process of measuring and the approximate nature of the results obtained. The approximate nature of measurement could be a new and disturbing concept for some students, so do not slight either section.

Lesson 2. (Secs. 9-3, 9-4, and 9-5)
The emphasis on the approximate nature of measurement is continued, and then attention is directed to an analysis of direct and indirect techniques of making measurements. The basic significance of each type of measurement is important. The discussion of crude but historically significant units of measure lays the foundation for the discussion of standard units in the next lesson.

Lesson 3. (Secs. 9-6 and 9-7)
The need for and the use of standard units of measure require no emphasis for significance. The historical struggle for efficient standard units gives an orientation for appreciation of their indispensability. Practice in the use of denominate numbers is of considerable practical value.

Lesson 4. (Sec. 9-8)
With this section new problems in the use of number arise. Many students seem to be unfamiliar with the concepts of precision and accuracy as they apply to measurement numbers. Develop each concept, along with the companion concepts of apparent error, relative error, and per cent of error, with great care. The concept of significant digits is also essential and demands careful development.

Lesson 5. (Sec. 9-9)
This new form for writing very large or very small numbers will be new for many. It is convenient, time saving, error preventing, and of great importance, particularly in the study of science. This is an important section and demands detailed attention before attempting Section 9-11.

Lesson 6. (Secs. 9-10 and 9-11)
The major problems in these two sections are concerned with what precision and accuracy can be justified in numbers that result from those computations involving approximate numbers. While other rules can be used, those given here are simply stated and produce justified results. Much practice in their use should be required.

Lesson 7. (Sec. 9-12)
The techniques of trigonometry provide powerful tools for making indirect measurements. This section develops the tangent and cotangent ratios. These are reciprocally related ratios. In actual practice the tangent ratio is the one most generally used. It should be made clear to the student just how the ratio and the angle are related to each other. It should also be pointed out that there are basic reasons for associating the names tangent and cotangent with the respective ratios. These are not

artificial ratios with artificial names.

Lesson 8. (Sec. 9-13)
Similarly the sine and cosine ratios have real significance and the association of the names is significant, as can be seen from the figure and the etymology of the words. The sine and cosine are related to each other, but the relation is Pythagorean, and not reciprocal.

This section should be related to the preceding section in exercises designed to emphasize the structure of a sine-cosine problem. In actual practice the sine and tangent prove to be the more frequently used functions.

Lesson 9. (Sec. 9-14)
Trigonometric indentities are of great importance in the study of more advanced work in mathematics. The basic identities are presented here along with a few exercises for practice in their use. Work with identities can be very interesting and challenging. Note carefully the precaution stated in the third way of dealing with identities. The possibility of reversing the steps is essential. The identity has not been established until one can guarantee that the steps can be reversed.

Lesson 10. (Sec. 9-15)
The use of the table of natural functions will require quite a bit of detailed treatment, especially in those cases calling for interpolation. The fact that the sine and tangent functions increase with the angle while the cosine and cotangent decrease with the angle must be dealt with precisely and followed with a great deal of practice.

Lesson 11. (Sec. 9-16)
Only the fundamental statistical measures are discussed in this section. Distinctions between the mean, median, and mode as measures of central tendency are discussed and illustrated. The variance and standard deviation are developed as measures of variability.

Opportunities for extended study in measurement, trigonometric identities, and statistical measures are provided at the end of the chapter.

CHAPTER 10. THE CONCEPTS OF RELATION AND FUNCTION
(11 lessons)

It is very fitting to draw this discussion of basic concepts of mathematics to a close with a brief but fundamental treatment of two of the most important of all such concepts, namely the concepts of relation and function. After the definition and a general discussion of these two closely related concepts, the context of a cartesian frame of reference is used for a more complete and detailed treatment of their most elementary forms, the linear function and the linear inequality.

Lessons 1-2. (Secs. 10-1 and 10-2)
After a careful review introduced by the first nine guideline questions, these two sections should be studied jointly for mastery of the basic definitions of constant, variable, ordered pair, relation, function, domain,

and <u>range</u>. These words constitute the major portion of the vocabulary of this entire chapter. These definitions are framed here to be consistent with the modern usage of each term considered.

Lesson 3. (Sec. 10-3)
The simplest of the functions, involving both a dependent and an independent variable, is the <u>linear</u> <u>function</u>. Note carefully that the <u>constant</u> <u>function</u> and the <u>constant</u> <u>relation</u> are not considered special cases of the linear function. Other important concepts of this section are the <u>slope</u> and <u>y-intercept</u> of the linear function, the <u>zero</u> <u>of</u> <u>the</u> <u>function</u>, and the <u>parameters</u> (<u>arbitrary</u> <u>constants</u>) of its formula.

Lesson 4. (Sec. 10-4)
Closely associated with the linear function is the more general concept of the <u>linear</u> <u>equation</u>, and its various forms. The techniques of determining the <u>graph</u> of the linear equation and the linear function are very fundamental, as are the techniques for determining the formula of such an equation or function satisfying certain specified conditions.

Lesson 5. (Sec. 10-5)
This section develops the theory of systems of two linear equations in two unknowns, giving due emphasis to the relative positions of the lines that are the graphs of the equations. The full significance of consistency and inconsistency of such systems must be developed. While the entire discussion is restricted to two equations in two variables, the principles and concepts are capable of generalization to systems of many equations in many variables. This fact underscores even more strongly the great importance of this section.

Lesson 6. (Sec. 10-6)
One of the more important developments of the modern emphasis in mathematics is to direct attention to the consideration of the <u>inequality</u> <u>relation</u>. This section deals with inequalities involving one and two variables, and systems of two inequalities involving two variables. The use of the line interval gives meaning to the inequality in one variable, while the use of half planes and intersection of half planes helps to bring out the full significance of inequalities in two variables. This section will be a source of difficulty to many, and demands very careful development. Pay special attention to the fact that although the inequality relation does possess the transitive property, it is neither reflexive nor symmetric. Also give strong emphasis to the contrasts in Theorems 10-4 and 10-5. These are spots where work with inequalities can become difficult. They demand precaution and care in treatment.

Lesson 7. (Sec. 10-7)
The three types of variation (<u>direct</u>, <u>inverse</u>, and <u>joint</u>) need to be kept clearly distinguished from each other. The language used in describing a particular situation usually clearly keys one in to the type involved. This means, of course, that one needs to learn this language and how to interpret its implications. While thorough understanding and competent use

of the constant of proportionality are of great importance for work with variation problems, the use of the concepts of ratio and proportion is not to be overlooked. In fact their use should be encouraged.

Lesson 8. (Sec. 10-8)

The statistical graph, in contrast to the function graph, attempts to portray relations and comparisons that are quantitative in character, but not necessarily susceptible to formula representation. Each type of graph (broken-line, bar, and circle) has certain distinguishing characteristics and can be used to portray certain types of quantitative information. For intelligent use of such graphs, whether construction or interpretation, the student needs to have a thorough understanding of these characteristics.

Lessons 9-10. (Sec. 10-9)

There is no greater trouble spot in any area of mathematical study than the solution of verbal problems. Now that the student has had the opportunity to become familiar with some of the elementary, yet very fundamental, tools to be used in problem solving, this section directs his attention to methods of analysis of problem situations and techniques for determining what tools are to be used in arriving at a solution.

While intuitive reasoning and induction can play an important part in dealing with problem situations, in the final analysis the solution is obtained through efficient use of the processes of deductive reasoning. An attempt is made in this section to give appropriate emphasis to each of these procedures. Do not rush through the treatment of the context to get to the problems. Study the context very carefully first before paying any attention whatsoever to the problems. They are placed at the end of the section not by accident but by reason. Pay particular emphasis to the fact that the process of solving a problem is never finished until the obtained solution has been checked in the given problem situation. It is not sufficient even to check the solution in the derived equations. It is well to do this, but the final check is always in the original problem situation.

Lesson 11. (Semester Review)

This last lesson is reserved for a concentrated oral review of the entire semester's work. Since Chapters 6-10 have dealt with concepts of number, geometry, and algebra, the students probably will need some assistance in organizing the material. The real number line and the cartesian frame of reference can be used as effective aids in accomplishing such an organization.

In actuality lessons 9 and 10 should have served as review aids in that the solution of problems demands the use of techniques developed in previous chapters of the book.

ANSWERS TO EVEN-NUMBERED PROBLEMS

IN TEXT

Sec. 1-1, page 10

2. (a) $O = \{o \mid o$ is an odd integer$\}$.
    (b) $T = \{t \mid t$ is a positive even integer less than 13$\}$.
    (c) $R = \{r \mid r$ is a state of the United States bordering on the Pacific ocean$\}$.
    (d) $V = \{v \mid v$ is a vowel of the English alphabet$\}$.
    (e) $A = \{s \mid s$ is a symbol to represent "three," using only positive integers and addition$\}$.
    (f) $B = \{b \mid b$ is an odd integer between 4 and 20$\}$.
    (g) $P = \{p \mid p$ is a one-digit positive integer$\}$.
    (h) $Z = \{z \mid z$ is an integer$\}$.

4. Yes. ϕ is a symbol for the empty set. $\{\phi\}$ is not an empty set, since it contains ϕ as an element.

6. (a) $B \cap P = \{5, 7, 9\}$; (b) $O \cup E = O$; (c) $G \cap M = \{\text{Texas}\}$.
    (d) $B - P = \{11, 13, 15, 17, 19\}$.
    (e) $B \cup S = \{5, 6, 7, 8, 9, 10, 11, 12, 13, 14, 15, 16, 17, 18, 19\}$.
    (f) $B \cap S = \{7, 9, 11, 13, 15, 17, 19\}$.

8. $A \cup U = U$; $A \cap U = A$.

10. $A \cup \sim A = U$; $A \cap \sim A = \phi$.

12. The diagrams shown are not necessarily the only correct diagrams.

(a)
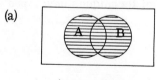

$A \cup B = B \cup A$

(b)
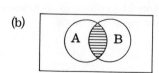

$A \cap B = B \cap A$

(c)

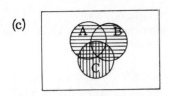

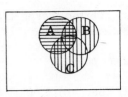

$A \cup B \equiv$, C |||

$A \equiv$, $B \cup C$ |||

$(A \cup B) \cup C$ any shading

$A \cup (B \cup C)$ any shading

(d)

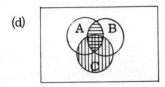

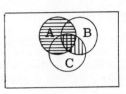

$A \cap B$, $\equiv C$ |||

$A \equiv$, $B \cap C$ |||

$(A \cap B) \cap C$ #

$A \cap (B \cap C)$ #

(e)

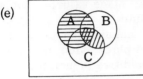

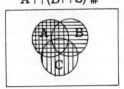

A |||, $B \cap C$ ///

$A \cup B \equiv$, $A \cup C$ |||

$A \cup (B \cap C)$ any shading

$(A \cup B) \cap (A \cup C)$ #

(f)

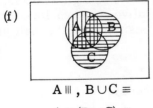

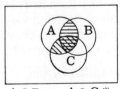

A |||, $B \cup C \equiv$

$A \cap B \equiv$, $A \cap C$ \\\

$A \cap (B \cup C)$ #

$(A \cap B) \cup (A \cap C)$ any shading

Sec. 1-4, page 18

12. (Answers in columns to correspond to numbers in the exercise)

ordinal	cardinal
cardinal	cardinal
ordinal	cardinal
ordinal	ordinal
cardinal	cardinal
ordinal	ordinal

14. {Diana, Marly}, {Diana, Marly, Cathy},
{Diana, Marly, Cathy, Carol, Sharon},
{Diana, Marly, Cathy, Carol, Sharon, Linda}.

16. (a) Vertoo, perpo-trang   (b) Trangoo, sar
    (c) saroo, trango   (d) Sarong, vertoo, trango-sar

Sec. 2-3, page 28

2. (a) 788; (b) 5,005; (c) 30,040; (d) 40,101; (e) 86,003,834.

4. (a) 1,085; (b) 142; (c) 371; (d) 1,200; (e) 51,858.

6. They made no use of place value in their numeral systems.

Sec. 2-6, page 33

2. Ten is used as the base for grouping.

4. The Hindu-Arabic system uses ten as a base, very simple digit symbols, place value, a symbol (0) for the empty position, and the additive principle.

(a) The Mayan system used twenty as a base, except that one positional value was based on eighteen rather than on twenty, complex digit symbols that used five as a pattern of grouping, place value, a symbol (☉) for the empty position, and the additive principle.

(b) The Babylonian system used sixty and also ten as bases, no clear system of digit symbols, a modified form of place value, no symbol for the empty position, and the multiplicative and additive principles.

(c) The Egyptian system used ten as a base, no digit symbols but symbols for each different power of ten, no place value, no symbol for the empty position, and the additive principle.

(d) The Roman System used ten as a base, no digit symbols, a modified form of position value indicated by relative positions for smaller and larger numbers, no symbol for the empty position, and the multiplicative and additive principles.

6. Multiplied by ten.

8. Its position value is divided by one hundred.

Sec. 2-10, page 39

2. They represent exactly the same number.

4. (a) **84**; (b) **t00**; (c) **5302**; (d) **2et9**; (e) **tete**; (f) **e000**; (g) **t0t0**.

6. The extreme right position is ones place; each new positional value of the next position to the right by the base, which is **10**.

8. 10-ten means one group of ten units; **20-five** means two groups of five each.

10. (a) **564**; (b) **800**; (c) **te5** (if **t** is the symbol for ten and **e** is the symbol for eleven); (d) **abc** (if **a** is the symbol for forty-five, **b** for thirty, and **c** for fifty).

Sec. 3-7, page 55

2. The sum of two natural numbers is a natural number, and there is no ambiguity as to what it should be.

6. In the table no numerals other than **verto** numerals occur.

8. (a) I ⊥; ⊥ 0; I □ ⊥.

10. (a) I □ 0 □; (b) I Δ □; (c) I ⊥ Δ ⊥ ⊥.

12. They contain only numerals in each of the two bases, **five** and **eight**, and each table is symmetric with respect to the diagonal from the upper left corner to the lower right corner.

14. (a) **213**; (b) **23212**; (c) 2134; (d) 21143.

16. (a) **11010**; (b) 1010110; (c) **10010100**; (d) 10001011.

20. (a) **226**; (b) **1625**; (c) 15453; (d) 226005; (e) **64445**.

22. Each is one less than the base in value.

24. **6-seven; t-eleven.**

26. (a) **t8**; (b) **238**; (c) 138t; (d) **2t78**; (e) **23018**; (f) **341t0**.

Sec. 3-13, page 68

2. Each is the inverse operation of the other.

6.   Ten

x	0	1	2	3	4	5	6	7	8	9
0	0	0	0	0	0	0	0	0	0	0
1	0	1	2	3	4	5	6	7	8	9
2	0	2	4	6	8	10	12	14	16	18
3	0	3	6	9	12	15	18	21	24	27
4	0	4	8	12	16	20	24	28	32	36
5	0	5	10	15	20	25	30	35	40	45
6	0	6	12	18	24	30	36	42	48	54
7	0	7	14	21	28	35	42	49	56	63
8	0	8	16	24	32	40	48	56	64	72
9	0	9	18	27	36	45	54	63	72	81

Verto

x	0	I	⊥	Δ	□
0	0	0	0	0	0
I	0	I	⊥	Δ	□
⊥	0	⊥	□	I I	I Δ
Δ	0	Δ	I I	I □	⊥ ⊥
□	0	□	I Δ	⊥ ⊥	Δ I

Eight

x	0	1	2	3	4	5	6	7
0	0	0	0	0	0	0	0	0
1	0	1	2	3	4	5	6	7
2	0	2	4	6	10	12	14	16
3	0	3	6	11	14	17	22	25
4	0	4	10	14	20	24	30	34
5	0	5	12	17	24	31	36	43
6	0	6	14	22	30	36	44	52
7	0	7	16	25	34	43	52	61

Twelve

x	0	1	2	3	4	5	6	7	8	9	t	e
0	0	0	0	0	0	0	0	0	0	0	0	0
1	0	1	2	3	4	5	6	7	8	9	t	e
2	0	2	4	6	8	t	10	12	14	16	18	1t
3	0	3	6	9	10	13	16	19	20	23	26	29
4	0	4	8	10	14	18	20	24	28	30	34	38
5	0	5	t	13	18	21	26	2e	34	39	42	47
6	0	6	10	16	20	26	30	36	40	46	50	56
7	0	7	12	19	24	2e	36	41	48	53	5t	65
8	0	8	14	20	28	34	40	48	54	60	68	74
9	0	9	16	23	30	39	46	53	60	69	76	83
t	0	t	18	26	34	42	50	5t	68	76	84	92
e	0	e	1t	29	38	47	56	65	74	83	92	t1

10. $77 \times 29 = 77 \times (16 + 8 + 4 + 1)$
$= (77 \times 16) + (77 \times 8) + (77 \times 4) + (77 \times 1)$
$= 2{,}233.$

12. (a) $63 \times 36 = (63 \times 4) \times 9 = (63 \times 9) \times 4 = 2{,}268.$
(b) $85 \times 28 = (85 \times 4) \times 7 = (85 \times 7) \times 4 = 2{,}380.$
(c) $272 \times 54 = (272 \times 6) \times 9 = (272 \times 9) \times 6 = 14{,}688.$

14. (a)

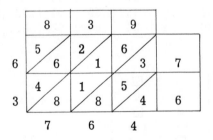

(b)

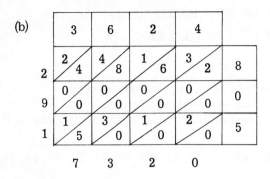

(c)

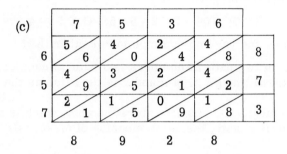

16. (a) t912; (b) 26ee701; (c) t7t16742.

18. 306t-twelve; 12222-eight; | △⊥0△ | – verto; 40214-six.

20. 3,798-ten; || 0 | □ △ – verto; 2246-twelve; 25330-six.

22. (a) 1,512; (b) 128,520.

Sec. 4-5, page 93

2. Decomposition—In each digit position, when a larger number is to be subtracted from a smaller number, one unit of the next position to the left is decomposed into 10 units and thus used to make the subtraction possible.

Deduction—The smaller number is taken away (deducted) from the larger number.

Diminution—The larger is diminished by the smaller number.

Comparison—Subtraction tells how much larger or how much smaller one number is than another.

4. (a) No. 1 + 1 = 2 and (−1, + (−1) = −2. 2 and −2 are not elements of the set.

(b) No. 1 − (−1) = 2 and (−1) −1 = −2.

(c) Yes. Under multiplication the only results possible are 1, 0, and −1, which are elements of the set.

6. 1 and 3 are odd integers and 1 + 3 = 4. Also, 3 − 1 = 2. 4 and 2 are not odd integers.

12. (a) **320**; (b) **132**; (c) **43**; (d) **221**; (e) **11**; (f) **133**.

14. (a) | 0 ⊥; (b) | 0 △; (c) | ⊥ |; (d) | ⊥ ⊥ □.

Sec. 4-6, page 101

2. (a) Not an integral domain; has no multiplicative identity.

(b) Not an integral domain; has no additive identity.

(c) Not an integral domain; has neither an additive identity nor additive inverses.

4. 2, 3, 5, 7, 11, 13, 17, 19, 23, 29, 31, 37, 41, 43, 47, 53, 59, 61, 67, 71,
73, 79, 83, 89, 97.

6. 1. They are relatively prime integers.

8. $24 = 2 \cdot 2 \cdot 2 \cdot 3$; $28 = 2 \cdot 2 \cdot 7$; $100 = 2 \cdot 2 \cdot 5 \cdot 5$; G.C.F. = 4.

10. These are prime numbers and have no common factor other than 1.

12. (a) Yes, since the g.c.f. of two natural numbers is a natural number.

(b) Yes, since $(a, b) = (b, a)$, the g.c.f. of a and b is the same as the
g.c.f. of b and a.

(c) Yes, since$((a, b), c)$ means the largest natural number which is a
factor of a, b, and c, and this is exactly the same meaning of $(a, (b, c))$.

26.

Base

Numeral	**two**	**three**	**five**	**seven**	ten	**twelve**
2	n	p	p	p	p	p
10	p	p	p	p	c	c
11	p	c	c	c	p	p
23	n	n	p	p	p	c
32	n	n	p	p	c	c
47	n	n	n	n	p	c
54	n	n	n	c	c	c

Sec. 5-5, page 124

2. $a/0 = b$ if and only if $b \cdot 0 = a$. This is a true statement if and only if
$a = 0$ in which case b can be any number.

4. Division is the inverse process to multiplication, so the tables can be
used to find the quotient of the product by either factor.

6. (a) $2{,}467 = 35 \times 70 + 17$; (b) $24{,}531 = 117 \times 209 + 78$; (c) $71{,}245 =
403 \times 176 + 317$.

8. (a) Excess of nines in $35 = 8$; in 70, it is 7; in 17, it is 8. $8 \times 7 + 8 =
64$. The excess of nines in 64 is 1, which is the same as the excess in
2,467

(b) Excess of nines in 117 is 0; in 209 it is 2, and in 78 it is 6. $0 \times
2 + 6 = 6$, which is the same as the excess of nines in 24,531.

(c) The excess of nines in 403 is 7; in 176 it is 5, and in 317 it is 2.
$7 \times 5 + 2 = 37$. The excess of nines in 37 is 1, which is the same as the excess of nines in 71,245.

14. (a) $20 = 2 \cdot 2 \cdot 5$; $35 = 5 \times 7$; $75 = 3 \times 5 \times 5$. g.c.d. = 5.
 (b) $42 = 2 \cdot 3 \cdot 7$; $56 = 2 \cdot 2 \cdot 2 \cdot 7$; $70 = 2 \cdot 5 \cdot 7$. g.c.d. $= 2 \cdot 7 = 14$.
 (c) $66 = 2 \cdot 3 \cdot 11$; $150 = 2 \cdot 3 \cdot 5 \cdot 5$; $210 = 2 \cdot 3 \cdot 5 \cdot 7$;
$300 = 2 \cdot 2 \cdot 3 \cdot 5 \cdot 5$. g.c.d. $= 2 \cdot 3 = 6$.
 (d) $132 = 2 \cdot 2 \cdot 3 \cdot 11$; $165 = 3 \cdot 5 \cdot 11$; $231 = 3 \cdot 7 \cdot 11$;
$297 = 3 \cdot 3 \cdot 3 \cdot 11$. g.c.d. $= 3 \cdot 11 = 33$.

16. (a) 37; (b) 156; (c) 5; (d) 251.

18. (a) **18 R 30**; (b) **16t R 4**; (c) **e1 R 34**.

20. (a) **154 R 2**; (b) **115 R 22**; (c) **213 R 252**.

Seven

22.

x	0	1	2	3	4	5	6
0	0	0	0	0	0	0	0
1	0	1	2	3	4	5	6
2	0	2	4	6	11	13	15
3	0	3	6	12	15	21	24
4	0	4	11	15	22	26	33
5	0	5	13	21	26	34	42
6	0	6	15	24	33	42	51

(a) 1,859-ten; **24414-five**; 10te-twelve.
(b) $\perp$ | $\square$ $\triangle$ $\perp$ 0-**verto**; **16444-eight**; **4398-twelve**.

Sec. 5-11, page 135

2. A fraction is a symbol which represents the quotient of one integer divided by another integer.

4.

Use	Numerator	Denominator
(a) Part of a unit	Number of parts taken	Number of parts into which the unit is divided
(b) Part of a group	Number in the group	Number of parts into which group is divided
(c) Quotient	Dividend	Divisor
(d) Ratio	Number of equal parts in one number being compared	Number of equal parts in other number being compared
(e) Number	Dividend	Divisor

6. Both numerator and denominator of a fraction may be multiplied or divided by the same number without changing the value of the fraction. The reason this works is that multiplication and division are inverse operations, and a fraction represents the quotient of one number divided by another number.

8. Division.

10. $\dfrac{5}{5}, \dfrac{3}{4}, \dfrac{2}{3}, \dfrac{5}{8}, \dfrac{1}{2}, \dfrac{3}{7}.$

12. (a) $\left(\dfrac{3}{4} + \dfrac{5}{6}\right) + \dfrac{1}{2} = \dfrac{3 \cdot 6 + 4 \cdot 5}{4 \cdot 6} + \dfrac{1}{2} = \dfrac{19}{12} + \dfrac{1}{2} = \dfrac{19 \cdot 2 + 12 \cdot 1}{12 \cdot 2} = \dfrac{25}{12}$

$\dfrac{3}{4} + \left(\dfrac{5}{6} + \dfrac{1}{2}\right) = \dfrac{3}{4} + \dfrac{5 \cdot 2 + 6 \cdot 1}{6 \cdot 2} = \dfrac{3}{4} + \dfrac{4}{3} = \dfrac{3 \cdot 3 + 4 \cdot 4}{4 \cdot 3} = \dfrac{25}{12}$

(b) $\left(\dfrac{7}{5} + \dfrac{2}{3}\right) + \dfrac{8}{15} = \dfrac{7 \cdot 3 + 5 \cdot 2}{5 \cdot 3} + \dfrac{8}{15} = \dfrac{31}{15} + \dfrac{8}{15} = \dfrac{39}{15} = \dfrac{13}{5}$

$\dfrac{7}{5} + \left(\dfrac{2}{3} + \dfrac{8}{15}\right) = \dfrac{7}{5} + \dfrac{2 \cdot 15 + 3 \cdot 8}{3 \cdot 15} = \dfrac{7}{5} + \dfrac{18}{15} = \dfrac{7 \cdot 15 + 5 \cdot 18}{5 \cdot 15} = \dfrac{13}{5}.$

A general proposition, or rule, cannot be proved by citing any number of specific cases in which it works.

14. Multiplication by a fraction is equivalent to multiplication by the numerator and division by the denominator. Each of these two numbers thus is an operator, rather than a number upon which an operation is performed.

16. (a) $\dfrac{3}{4} \times \dfrac{8}{27} = \dfrac{3 \times 8}{4 \times 27} = \dfrac{24}{108} = \dfrac{2}{9}; \quad \dfrac{8}{27} \times \dfrac{3}{4} = \dfrac{8 \times 3}{27 \times 4} = \dfrac{24}{108} = \dfrac{2}{9}.$

(b) $\dfrac{5}{6} \times \dfrac{7}{9} = \dfrac{5 \times 7}{6 \times 9} = \dfrac{35}{54}; \quad \dfrac{7}{9} \times \dfrac{5}{6} = \dfrac{7 \times 5}{9 \times 6} = \dfrac{35}{54}.$

A general proposition, or rule, cannot be proved by citing any number of specific cases in which it works.

20. (a) $5 + 7 = 12$; $7 + 5 = 12$; $5 \times 7 = 35$; $7 \times 5 = 35$; $(5 + 7) + 12 = 12 + 12 = 24$; $5 + (7 + 12) = 5 + 19 = 24$; $(5 \times 7) \times 12 = 35 \times 12 = 420$; $5 \times (7 \times 12) = 5 \times 84 = 420$; $5 \times (7 + 12) = 5 \times 19 = 95$; $(5 \times 7) + (5 \times 12) = 35 + 60 = 95.$

(f) $\left(\dfrac{-3}{5}\right) + \dfrac{1}{2} = \dfrac{-3}{5} + \dfrac{1}{2} = \dfrac{(-3) \cdot 2 + 5 \cdot 1}{5 \cdot 2} = \dfrac{-6 + 5}{10} = \dfrac{-1}{10}.$

$\dfrac{1}{2} + \left(\dfrac{-3}{5}\right) = \dfrac{1 \cdot 5 + 2 \cdot (-3)}{2 \cdot 5} = \dfrac{5 - 6}{10} = \dfrac{-1}{10}.$

$\left(\dfrac{-3}{5} + \dfrac{1}{2}\right) + \dfrac{-4}{7} = \dfrac{-1}{10} + \dfrac{-4}{7} = \dfrac{(-1) \cdot 7 + 10 \cdot (-4)}{10 \cdot 7}$

$= \dfrac{(-7) + (-40)}{70} = \dfrac{-47}{70}.$

$$\frac{-3}{5} + \left(\frac{1}{2} + \frac{-4}{7}\right) = \frac{-3}{5} + \frac{1 \cdot 7 + 2 \cdot (-4)}{2 \cdot 7} = \frac{-3}{5} + \frac{7 - 8}{14} = \frac{-3}{5} + \frac{-1}{14}$$

$$= \frac{(-3) \cdot 14 + 5 \cdot (-1)}{5 \cdot 14} = \frac{-42 + (-5)}{70} = \frac{-47}{70}.$$

$$\frac{-3}{5} \cdot \frac{-4}{7} = \frac{(-3) \cdot (-4)}{5 \cdot 7} = \frac{12}{35}.$$

$$\frac{-4}{7} \cdot \frac{-3}{5} = \frac{(-4) \cdot (-3)}{7 \cdot 5} = \frac{12}{35}.$$

$$\left(\frac{-3}{5} \cdot \frac{1}{2}\right) \cdot \left(\frac{-4}{7}\right) = \frac{(-3) \cdot 1}{5 \cdot 2} \cdot \frac{-4}{7} = \frac{-3}{10} \cdot \frac{-4}{7} = \frac{(-3) \cdot (-4)}{10 \cdot 7} = \frac{12}{70} = \frac{6}{35}.$$

$$\frac{-3}{5} \cdot \left(\frac{1}{2} \cdot \frac{-4}{7}\right) = \frac{-3}{5} \cdot \frac{1 \cdot (-4)}{2 \cdot 7} = \frac{-3}{5} \cdot \frac{-4}{14} = \frac{(-3) \cdot (-4)}{5 \cdot 14} = \frac{12}{70} = \frac{6}{35}.$$

$$\frac{-3}{5} \cdot \left(\frac{1}{2} + \frac{-4}{7}\right) = \frac{-3}{5} \cdot \frac{1 \cdot 7 + 2 \cdot (-4)}{2 \cdot 7} = \frac{-3}{5} \cdot \frac{7 + (-8)}{14}$$

$$= \frac{-3}{5} \cdot \frac{-1}{14} = \frac{(-3) \cdot (-1)}{5 \cdot 14} = \frac{3}{70}.$$

$$\left(\frac{-3}{5} \cdot \frac{1}{2}\right) + \left(\frac{-3}{5} \cdot \frac{-4}{7}\right) = \frac{(-3) \cdot 1}{5 \cdot 2} + \frac{(-3) \cdot (-4)}{5 \cdot 7} = \frac{-3}{10} + \frac{12}{35}$$

$$= \frac{(-3) \cdot (35) + 10 \cdot 12}{10 \cdot 35} = \frac{(-105) + (120)}{350}$$

$$= \frac{15}{350} = \frac{3}{70}.$$

22. Neither addition and division nor subtraction and division are inverse operations.

24. In a field, for each nonzero element a, there exists a unique inverse element 1/a such that $a \cdot 1/a = 1/a \cdot a = \overline{1}$.
    This is not true in an integral domain. Instead, in an integral domain if ac = bc and c ≠ 0 then it follows that a = b.

26. With the exception of the inverse postulate, the field postulates are the same as those for an integral domain. Furthermore, the inverse postulate guarantees that the cancellation law for multiplication holds, as it must in an integral domain.

Sec. 5-19, page 152.

2. In a terminating decimal there is a finite number of digits. A repeating decimal has an infinite number of digits that repeat in a specific pattern.

4. (a) 265.5282; (b) 0.0281466; (c) 1266.543; (d) 97.528.

6. The denominators are not of the form $2^m 5^n$.
   (a) 0.$\overline{428571}$; (b) 0.8$\overline{3}$; (c) 0.1$\overline{6}$; (d) 9.196$\overline{428571}$; (e) 0.1$\overline{6}$; (f) 0.02$\overline{6}$.

8. $10 \times 0.5\overline{0} = 5.0\overline{0}$ $10 \times 0.4\overline{9} = 4.9\overline{9}$
    $\underline{1 \times 0.5\overline{0} = 0.50}$ $\underline{1 \times 0.4\overline{9} = .4\overline{9}}$

    $9 \times 0.5\overline{0} = 4.5$ $9 \times 0.4\overline{9} = 4.5$

    $0.5\overline{0} = \dfrac{4.5}{9} = 0.5$ $0.4\overline{9} = \dfrac{4.5}{9} = 0.5$

10. (a) $0.000\frac{1}{3}$ too large. (b) $0.6666\overline{7}$.

12. (a) In situation B the base (enrollment) is the same in each case. This is not true in situation A.
    (b) 14.   (c) 73.7%.

Sec. 6-6, page 171

2. A rational number can be expressed either as a finite decimal or as an infinite repeating decimal. An irrational number can be expressed only as an infinite nonrepeating decimal. More simply, a rational number can be expressed as the quotient of two integers, while an irrational number cannot.

6. No. It has neither an additive identity nor a multiplicative identity. Both 0 and 1 are rational numbers.

12. $-2, \quad -\sqrt[3]{2}, \quad -1.2\overline{5}, \quad -1.25, \quad 0.857, \quad \dfrac{6}{7}, \quad 0.85\overline{7}, \quad 1.4, \quad 1.414, \quad \sqrt[3]{3}$.

14. (a) $|x| \le 1$; (b) $|x - 4| \le 1$; (c) $|x| < 5$; (d) $|x| \le \sqrt{3}$.

18. (a) $1 + 2i$; (b) $-\dfrac{6}{25} - \dfrac{17}{25}i$; (c) $-\dfrac{3}{13} + \dfrac{28}{13}i$.

Sec. 7-4, page 187

2. No. 4. Yes. 6. Yes. 8. Yes. 10. No. 12. Yes. 14. Yes. 16. Yes. 18. Yes.

30. A number is divisible by 125 if and only if the last three digits form a number which is divisible by 125.

32. A number is divisible by 15 if and only if it is divisible both by 3 and by 5.
    A number is divisible by 18 if and only if it is divisible both by 2 and by 9.
    A number is divisible by 22 if and only if it is divisible both by 2 and 11.
    A number is divisible by 24 if and only if it is divisible both by 3 and by 8.

34. 2, 3, 4, 6, 9, 12, 18.

36. 2, 3, 4, 5, 6, 12, 15.

38. 2, 4, 5.

40. 2, 3, 4, 5, 6, 8, 12, 15, 24.

42. 2, 3, 4, 5, 6, 9, 12, 15, 18.

44. In base **six**: A number is divisible by **2** if and only if the digit in ones places is divisble by **2**.

The test for divisibility by **3** is the same as that for **2**.

A number is divisible by **4** if and only if **2** times the digit in the base position, plus the digit in ones place, is a number divisible by **4**; or, if and only if the last two digits to the right form a number divisible by **4**.

A number is divisible by **5** if and only if the sum of its digits is a number divisible by **5**.

Sec. 8-3, page 202

2. All statements are true with the exception of (c).

4. Planes M and N are coincident planes.

10. There are 6 lines and 4 planes.

14. The union of two half lines, with a common boundary point, is a line, with one point (the boundary point) deleted.

The union of two half planes with a common edge is a plane, with one line (the common edge) deleted.

The union of two half spaces with a common face is all space, with one plane (the common face) deleted.

16. (a) $3; \ 1\frac{1}{3}; \ 3\frac{1}{6}; \ 1\frac{1}{6}; \ 3\frac{1}{2}.$

(b) H is two units distance from M and from C.

(c) $C; \ O; \ H; \ A$.

(d) $\sqrt{5}; \ \sqrt{3}; \ \sqrt{3} + \sqrt{5}; \ 1 + \sqrt{3}; \ 2\frac{1}{2} - \sqrt{3}.$

Sec. 8-4, page 211

6. In the pyramid $K\text{-}LMN$:

(a) 4 points; 6 lines; 4 planes.

(b) 12 plane angles: *KLM; KLN; MLN; KML; KMN; LMN; KNM; KNL; MNL; LKM; LKN; MKN.*

(c) 6 dihedral angles: *M-LK-N; M-NK-L; L-MK-N; K-LM-N; K-MN-L; K-LN-M.*

In the rectangular solid;

(a) 8 points; 12 lines; 6 planes.

(b) 24 plane angles: *DAB; ABC; BCD; CDA; CFG; FGD; GDC; DCF; FEH; EHG; HGF; GFE; HEB; EBA; BAH; AHE; DAH; AHG; HGD; GDA; CBE; BEF; EFC; FCB.*

(c) 12 dihedral angles: *D-AB-E; A-HE-F; H-GF-C; G-DC-B; D-BC-E; C-BE-H; B-FE-H; D-FC-E; D-AH-E; A-HG-E; A-GD-F; G-AD-C.*

(d) ∠ *BAH* is the plane angle of the dihedral angle G-AD-C.

(e) *G-AD-C* is a right dihedral angle.

(f) No. The sides of the plane angle of a dihedral angle are respectively perpendicular to the edge of the dihedral angle.

(g) Two.

(h) Any line in space may be considered as the line of intersection of an infinite number of planes.

(i) Two. Postulate 8-6.

(j) Three.

(k) There is an infinite number of planes that pass through each point of space.

(l) Three. By Postulate 8-6 the intersection of two planes is a line. A third plane might then have only one point in common with this line.

10. (a) $80°$, $170°$; (b) $45°$, $135°$; (c) $30°$, $120°$; (d) $A°$, $(90 + A)°$.

12. (a) *CPN* and *BPM*.

(b) *APC* and *CPM*; *CPM* and *MPN*; *MPN* and *NPB*; *NPB* and *BPD*; *APC* and *BPN*; *BPD* and *CPM*.

(c) *APC* and *CPB*; *DPB* and *CPB*; *CPM* and *MPD*.

(d) *APC* and *MPN*; *APC* and *DPB*; *DPB* and *MPN*; *CPN* and *BPN*.

Sec. 8-6, page 219

12. No. Honolulu is west longitude; Sydney is east longitude.

14. Natal, Brazil. The meridian for Natal is closer to the prime meridian than that for Camden.

Sec. 8-8, page 230

2. No.

8. (a) Δ *ABC* ~ Δ *EFD*.

(b) Δ *ABC* ~ Δ *DEF*.

(c) No similar triangles.

(d) Δ *ABC* ~ Δ *FDE*.

(e) No similar triangles.

(f) Δ *ABC* ~ Δ *EDF*.

(g) Δ *ABC* ~ Δ *EDF*.

(h) No similar triangles.

(i) Δ *ABC* ~ Δ *DEF*.

10. DF = 48; EF = 24.

Sec. 8-10, page 234

2. Yes. ∠s *DAC* and *BAC* can be shown to be corresponding angles of congruent triangles; similarly, for ∠s *DCA* and *BCA*.

4. ∠ *QPR* ≅ ∠ *SPR*; ∠ *QRS* ≅ ∠ *SPR*.

No. If Δ *SPR* is folded over along the diagonal $\overline{PR}$, it will not coincide with Δ *QRP*.

10. (a) <u>Circle</u>—Each diameter is an axis of symmetry; the center of the circle is the center of symmetry.

(b) Sphere—Each diameter is an axis of symmetry; the center of the circle is the center of symmetry.

(c) Isosceles triangle—The altitude from the point of intersection of the two equal sides is an axis of symmetry; there is no center of symmetry.

(d) Scalene triangle—There is neither an axis nor a center of symmetry.

(e) Equilateral triangle—Each altitude is an axis of symmetry; the point of intersection of the three altitudes is the center of symmetry.

(f) Quadrilateral with no two sides equal—There is neither an axis nor a center of symmetry.

(g) Square—Each diagonal and each line joining the midpoints of opposite sides is an axis of symmetry; the common point of intersection of these four lines is the center of symmetry.

(h) Rectangle—Each line joining the midpoints of opposite sides is an axis of symmetry; their point of intersection is the center of symmetry.

(i) Parallelogram—There is no axis of symmetry; the point of intersection of the diagonals is the center of symmetry.

(j) Rhombus—Each diagonal is an axis of symmetry; their point of intersection is the center of symmetry.

(k) Cube—There are thirteen axes of symmetry; their common point of intersection is the center of symmetry.

Sec. 9-2, page 253

2. Approximate; it is a measure of speed.
4. Could be either. If the seats are actually counted, then the number is exact. If it expresses an estimate, it is approximate.
6. Could be either. If it represents the result of an actual count, it is exact. If it expresses an estimate, it is approximate.
8. Approximate; it is a measure of distance.
10. Exact; it is based on exact definitions.
12. Exact; each number represents the result of a count.
14. Approximate; each number represents a measure.
16. Exact; it expresses an exact date in time.

Sec. 9-4, page 257

2. Each measure is subject to the many different sources of error present in making any measurement.

4. (a) It is the result of an estimate.
   (b) The seats might be counted.

6. Indirect.   8. Indirect.   10. Direct.
12. Indirect.   14. Indirect.   16. Direct.

Sec. 9-7, page 267

2. 1 in. = 0.0254 meter.

4. 41,900 wave lengths. This figure is obtained by using the answer to Exercise 2. A more precise relation between the inch and the meter would give a more precise result here.

6. 280,000,000,000,000 miles.

8. 0.000000000000000000000001673 gram.

10. 0.000000000000000000000001675 gram.

12. 34 hr 29 min 3̲0̲ sec or 1 da 10 hr 29 min 3̲0̲ sec.

14. 4 sq yd 3 sq ft 92 sq in.

16. 2 m 8 dm 1 cm 2 mm.

18. 2.812 meter; 2.163 gram.

20. 52 ft 8 in.   22. 17 gal 2 qt 1 pt.

24. 1 sq yd 3 sq ft 64 sq in. R 4 sq in.   26. 1m 5dm 1 cm.

28. 4 to 1.   30. 1 to 5.   32. 1.51 meter.   34. 1 to 5.

Sec. 9-11, page 279

2. 8 ft is correct to the nearest foot. It means 8 ft ± 0.5 ft or 8 ft ± $\frac{1}{2}$ ft, depending upon the graduations of the measuring instrument. 8.0 ft is correct to the nearest tenth of a foot. It means 8.0 ft ± 0.05 ft. 8.00 ft is correct to the nearest hundredth of a foot. It means 8.00 ft ± 0.005 ft.

4. 25,000 miles per hour.

6.

Exercise	Maximum Apparent error	Relative error	Per cent of error
(a)	0.5 in. or $\frac{1}{2}$ in.	1/198	0.5
(b)	$\frac{1}{2}$ pk	1/46	2
(c)	$\frac{1}{2}$ oz	1/330	0.3
(d)	$\frac{1}{2}$ sec	1/6990	0.01
(e)	$\frac{1}{2}$ pk	1/12	8
(f)	$\frac{1}{2}$ qt, or 1 pt	1/12	8
(g)	0.000005 in.	1/40	$2\frac{1}{2}$
(h)	0.0005 mi	1/234000	0.0004
(i)	0.05 sec	1/2704	0.04
(j)	500 mi	1/442	0.2
(k)*	$\frac{1}{2}$ dollar	1/20,000	0.005
(l)	0.05 in.	1/4040	0.02

*This answer is based on the assumption that the 10,000 is not the result of an exact count.

8. (a) 19 ft 6 in.;   (b) 42 ft 0̲ in.;   (c) 48.00 in.;   (d) 23 yd 1 ft 8 in.;
(e) 23 ft 0 in. (correct to the nearest ten inches)   (f) 1545.8 ft;   (g) 80̲ in.;
(h) 200.0 in.;   (i) 192.36 in.;   (j) 20.0 in.

10. Area, 167 sq ft;   perimeter, 97.28 ft.
     The area is found by multiplication, and the answer can be given correct
only to three significant figures. The perimeter is found by addition, and the
answer can be given correct to hundredths of a foot since each measure has
this precision.

12. (a) 1.50 in.   (b) 12.0 sq in.   (c) 1.80 in.

14. 74.7 in.

16. (a) 5×10^{-3} cm;   (b) 8.0×10^{23} molecules;   (c) 3.16×10^{-5} in.;
(d) 7.2×10^{-5} cm to 4.0×10^{-5} cm;   (e) 1.64100×10^{4} ft per sec;   (f) 4.839×10^{8} miles.

18. North Star: 2.8×10^{14} miles;   Alpha Centauri: 2.5×10^{13} miles.

20. 38.1 years.

Sec. 9-15, page 296

2. 65 ft.

16. $\sin 45° = 0.7071$; $\tan 75° = 3.732$; $\cos 58° = 0.5299$; $\cot 16° = 3.487$;
$\sin 67°12' = 0.9218$; $\cos 23°50' = 0.9147$; $\tan 24°45' = 0.4610$; $\cot 68°19' = 0.3976$.

18. 33°39';   49°2';   57°50̲';   57°3'.

20. 49.2 ft.   22. 30.81 ft.

Sec. 9-16, page 303

2. Mean, 6;   median, 6;   mode 5 and 7.

6. The second group has a bit higher level of IQ than the first group, while
the first group is a more homogeneous group, since its IQ scores are not so
widely scattered as those of the second group.

Sec. 10-2, page 317

2. No one of the three relations is transitive.

4. A function is a relation for which there is one and only one value of the
dependent variable (second element) which corresponds to each value of the
independent variable (first element).

6. Relations (b), (f), (g), (j), (m) are equivalence relations because they
are reflexive, symmetric, and transitive.
     (a) is not symmetric.
     (c) is neither reflexive nor symmetric.
     (d) is neither reflexive nor symmetric.

(e) has no one of the three properties.
(h) is not symmetric.
(i) has no one of the three properties.
(k) is neither reflexive nor transitive.
(l) is neither reflexive nor transitive.

8.

Exercise	Domain	Range
(a)	Set of all positive integers	Set of all positive even integers
(b)	Set of all positive integers	Set of all positive integers greater than 3
(c)	Set of all real numbers	Set of all real numbers
(d)	Set of all positive real numbers	Set of all real numbers
(e)	Set of all integers	Set of all odd integers
(f)	Set of all real numbers	Set of all real numbers
(g)	Set of all negative real numbers	Set of all negative real numbers

12. See graph on next page

16. (a) {(0,0); (1,3); (2,6); (3,9); (4,12); (5,15); (6,18); (7,21); (8,24); (9,27)}.
 (b) {(0,0); (1,1/5); (2,2/5); (3,3/5); (4,4/5); (5,1); (6,6/5); (7,7/5); (8,8/5); (9,9/5)}.
 (c) {(0,4); (1,5); (2,6); (3,7); (4,8); (5,9); (6,10); (7,11); (8,12); (9,13)
 (d) {(0,−1); (1,0); (2,1); (3,2); (4,3); (5,4); (6,5); (7,6); (8,7); (9,8)}.
 (e) {(0,0); (1,1/2); (2,1); (3,3/2); (4,2); (5,5/2); (6,3); (7,7/2); (8,4); (9,9/2)}.
 (f) {(0,−1); (1,1); (2,3); (3,5); (4,7); (5,9); (6,−11); (7,13); (8,15); (9,17)}.
 (g) {(0,−2); (1,0); (2,2); (3,4); (4,6); (5,8); (6,10); (7,12); (8,14); (9,16)}.
 (h) {(0,4); (1,4 1/3); (2,4 2/3); (3,5); (4,5 1/3); (5,5 2/3); (6,6); (7,6 1/3); (8,6 2/3); (9,7)}.
 (i) {(0,4/3); (1,5/3); (2,2); (3,7/3); (4,8/3); (5,3); (6,10/3); (7,11/3); (8,4); (9,13/3)}.

18. (a)

0	1	2	3	4	5	6	7	8	9
0	3	6	9	12	15	18	21	24	27

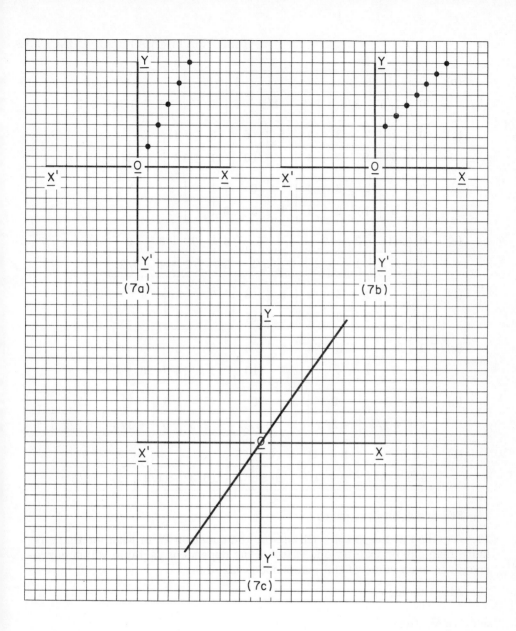

(b)

0	1	2	3	4	5	6	7	8	9
0	1/5	2/5	3/5	4/5	1	6/5	7/5	8/5	9/5

(c)

0	1	2	3	4	5	6	7	8	9
4	5	6	7	8	9	10	11	12	13

(d)

0	1	2	3	4	5	6	7	8	9
−1	0	1	2	3	4	5	6	7	8

(e)

0	1	2	3	4	5	6	7	8	9
0	1/2	1	3/2	2	5/2	3	7/2	4	9/2

(f)

0	1	2	3	4	5	6	7	8	9
−1	1	3	5	7	9	11	13	15	17

(g)

0	1	2	3	4	5	6	7	8	9
−2	0	2	4	6	8	10	12	14	16

(h)

0	1	2	3	4	5	6	7	8	9
4	4 1/3	4 2/3	5	5 1/3	5 2/3	6	6 1/3	6 2/3	7

(i)

0	1	2	3	4	5	6	7	8	9
4/3	5/3	2	7/3	8/3	3	10/3	11/3	4	13/3

20. See graph on next page.

22. A glance at the graph will answer the question as to whether there is more than one or exactly one value of the dependent variable which corresponds to each value of the independent variable.

28. All of them.

Sec. 10-4, page 332

2. Set $x = 0$ and solve for y.

4. If the y-intercept is k, the line passes through the point (o,k).

8. (a) $y = 2x$; (b) $y = 2x + 2$; (c) $y = 2x + 4$.

10. See graph. (Answers 33 a.)

12. $d = 60t$.

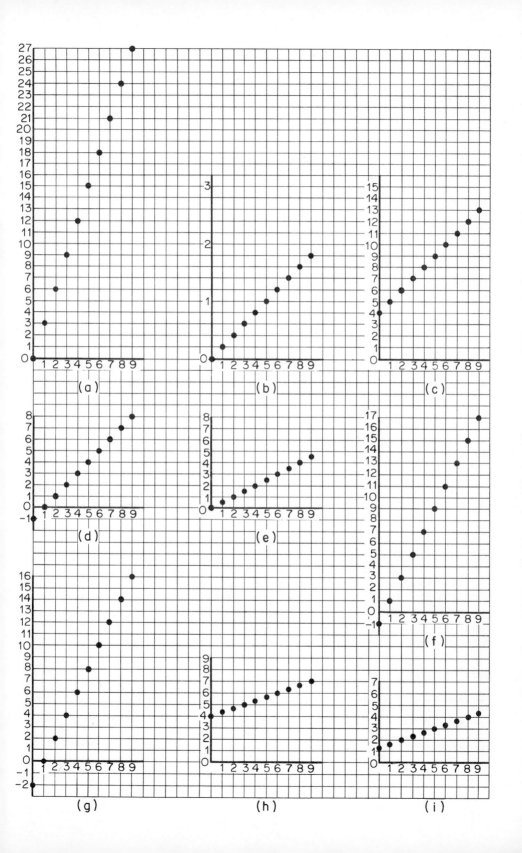

Sec. 10-5, page 339

2. $\{(x,y) \mid y = 4x - 8 \text{ and } x \text{ is a real number}\}$.

4. $x = 4, \quad y = 6$.

6. $\{(x,y) \mid y = x + 3 \text{ and } x \text{ is a real number}\}$.

8. Inconsistent.

10. $\{(x,y) \mid y = 1/4 \,(x - 8) \text{ and } x \text{ is a real number}\}$. (See graph on following page.)

12. $x = 1/2, \quad y = -3/2$.

14. $\{(x,y) \mid y = 7/3x + 4 \text{ and } x \text{ is a real number}\}$.

16. Inconsistent.

18. $\{(x,y) \mid y = 1.25\,x - 2.5 \text{ and } x \text{ is a real number}\}$.

20. Inconsistent.

Sec. 10-6, page 344

2. $\mid x \mid \le 5$.   4. $\mid x - 3/2 \mid < 3/2$.   6. $\mid x - 8 \mid \le 3$.

8. $\mid x + 3/2 \mid \le 5/2$.   10. $-1 \le x \le 1$.   12. $-1 \le x \le 3$.

14. $-7 < x < -3$.   16. $x < -1/2$.   18. $x < 1$.

20. $x \le 1$.   22.—36. (See graphs below.)

Sec. 10-7, page 347

2. $288\,\pi$.   4. 72 amperes; 0.48 ohm.

6. \$337.50; \$28.69.   8. 10.

Sec. 10-8, page 353

2. The bar graph primarily shows comparison without reference to trends. When the data are such that trends are indicated, they may be read from the graph. The broken-line graph primarily shows trends. Comparisons may be read from this graph. The circle graph shows comparisons of parts with parts of a whole and also with the whole.

Sec. 10-9, page 361

2. 4 1/2 hours.   4. \$15.20.   6. 378; 380.   8. 9; 15.   10. 18.4%

12. $x + y = -1$.   14. Length, 65 yd; width, 35 yd.   16. 80 girls, 100 boys.

18. \$5,000 at 4%; \$7,000 at 4 1/2%.   20. 72, airmail; 228, ordinary

mail.   22. 63 seconds.

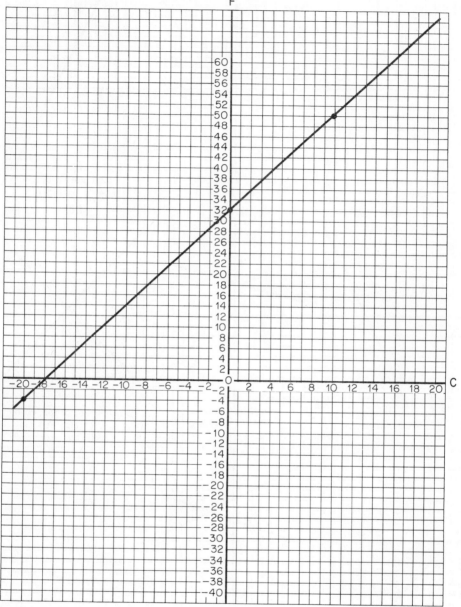

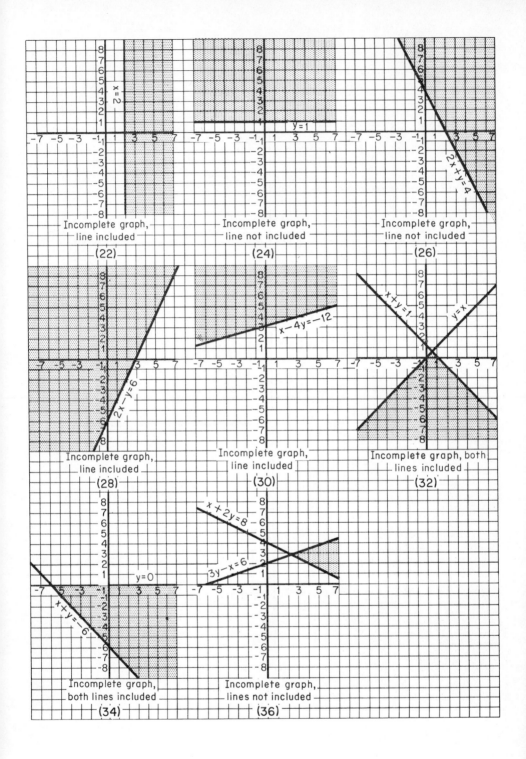

Incomplete graph, line included (22)

Incomplete graph, line not included (24)

Incomplete graph, line not included (26)

Incomplete graph, line included (28)

Incomplete graph, line included (30)

Incomplete graph, both lines included (32)

Incomplete graph, both lines included (34)

Incomplete graph, lines not included (36)